IF FOUND, PLEASE RETURN TO:

_____

_____

_____

_____

Research and Publications Planner

The Graduate Student's Guide to Publishing Academic Research

Jasmin M. Goodman

Created and published by The J. Michelle Group
Email: publishing@thejmichellegroup.com

ISBN 978-0-578-58066-1 (Paperback Edition)

Library of Congress Control Number: 2019914618

Disclaimer: This book is meant solely as a supplemental educational aid. In no event will Jasmin M. Goodman or The J. Michelle Group be liable for any harm, injury, or damages, including direct, indirect, incidental, special, consequential, or punitive arising out of or in connection with the use of information contained in this book.

First published in the United States of America in 2019 by The J. Michelle Group. First Printing, 2019.

How to Use This Guide

Created by a graduate student for graduate students, this research and publications planner is perfect for masters and doctoral students who are ready to take their research productivity to the next level. This carefully thought-out guide provides a structured method for brainstorming research projects and ideas. No more jotting down prospective publications in miscellaneous notebooks or in the margins of your assigned reading. Use this guide to keep track of class and conference papers, dissertation ideas, and future publications.

The following pages offer examples of how to use this workbook. As a note, each section can be completed in any order you choose.

PROPOSED TITLE

Use this section to jot down ideas for your title. This can be done last.

BRAINSTORM

This space is perfect for organizing your thoughts and writing down any initial questions or ideas.

STUDY JUSTIFICATION & SIGNIFICANCE

Why is your research important? How will it contribute to the existing literature?

THEORETICAL FRAMEWORK

What theory will you use?

POTENTIAL CO-AUTHORS

List any possible co-authors here.

KEY WORDS FOR LITERATURE REVIEW

What key words will you use to search for relevant literature?

METHODOLOGY

What method will best accomplish your research goals?

PROJECTED HYPOTHESES

Brainstorm any hypotheses here.

RESEARCH QUESTIONS

Jot any research questions here.

ANALYSIS PLAN

Brainstorm how you will analyze your data here. Identify possible data sources, statistical analyses, and tables and figures. Extra space is provided.

LIMITATIONS

As you are analyzing your data, quickly jot down any study limitations.

FUTURE DIRECTIONS

This section is for any future research opportunities you identify.

PROSPECTIVE PUBLICATIONS

List all potential publications here.

RESEARCH & WRITING SCHEDULE

Use this space to create a tough, but realistic, writing schedule.

Use this space for any additional ideas or research notes.

Let's Get Started!

PROPOSED TITLE

BRAINSTORM

STUDY JUSTIFICATION & SIGNIFICANCE

THEORETICAL FRAMEWORK

PROJECTED HYPOTHESES

POTENTIAL CO-AUTHORS

KEY WORDS FOR LITERATURE REVIEW

RESEARCH QUESTIONS

METHODOLOGY

ANALYSIS PLAN

LIMITATIONS

FUTURE DIRECTIONS

PROSPECTIVE PUBLICATIONS

RESEARCH & WRITING SCHEDULE

RESEARCH NOTES

PROPOSED TITLE

BRAINSTORM

STUDY JUSTIFICATION & SIGNIFICANCE

THEORETICAL FRAMEWORK

POTENTIAL CO-AUTHORS

KEY WORDS FOR LITERATURE REVIEW

METHODOLOGY

PROJECTED HYPOTHESES

RESEARCH QUESTIONS

ANALYSIS PLAN

LIMITATIONS

FUTURE DIRECTIONS

PROSPECTIVE PUBLICATIONS

RESEARCH & WRITING SCHEDULE

PROPOSED TITLE

BRAINSTORM

STUDY JUSTIFICATION & SIGNIFICANCE

THEORETICAL FRAMEWORK

POTENTIAL CO-AUTHORS

KEY WORDS FOR
LITERATURE REVIEW

METHODOLOGY

PROJECTED HYPOTHESES

RESEARCH QUESTIONS

ANALYSIS PLAN

LIMITATIONS

FUTURE DIRECTIONS

PROSPECTIVE PUBLICATIONS

RESEARCH & WRITING SCHEDULE

PROPOSED TITLE

BRAINSTORM

STUDY JUSTIFICATION & SIGNIFICANCE

THEORETICAL FRAMEWORK

PROJECTED HYPOTHESES

POTENTIAL CO-AUTHORS

KEY WORDS FOR LITERATURE REVIEW

RESEARCH QUESTIONS

METHODOLOGY

ANALYSIS PLAN

LIMITATIONS

FUTURE DIRECTIONS

PROSPECTIVE PUBLICATIONS

RESEARCH & WRITING SCHEDULE

PROSPECTIVE PUBLICATIONS

PROPOSED TITLE

BRAINSTORM

STUDY JUSTIFICATION & SIGNIFICANCE

THEORETICAL FRAMEWORK

POTENTIAL CO-AUTHORS

KEY WORDS FOR LITERATURE REVIEW

METHODOLOGY

PROJECTED HYPOTHESES

RESEARCH QUESTIONS

ANALYSIS PLAN

LIMITATIONS

FUTURE DIRECTIONS

PROSPECTIVE PUBLICATIONS

RESEARCH & WRITING SCHEDULE

PROPOSED TITLE

BRAINSTORM

STUDY JUSTIFICATION & SIGNIFICANCE

THEORETICAL FRAMEWORK

POTENTIAL CO-AUTHORS

KEY WORDS FOR LITERATURE REVIEW

METHODOLOGY

PROJECTED HYPOTHESES

RESEARCH QUESTIONS

ANALYSIS PLAN

LIMITATIONS

FUTURE DIRECTIONS

PROSPECTIVE PUBLICATIONS

RESEARCH & WRITING SCHEDULE

PROSPECTIVE PUBLICATIONS

RESEARCH NOTES

PROPOSED TITLE

BRAINSTORM

STUDY JUSTIFICATION & SIGNIFICANCE

THEORETICAL FRAMEWORK

PROJECTED HYPOTHESES

POTENTIAL CO-AUTHORS

KEY WORDS FOR LITERATURE REVIEW

RESEARCH QUESTIONS

METHODOLOGY

ANALYSIS PLAN

LIMITATIONS

FUTURE DIRECTIONS

PROSPECTIVE PUBLICATIONS

RESEARCH & WRITING SCHEDULE

RESEARCH NOTES

PROPOSED TITLE

BRAINSTORM

STUDY JUSTIFICATION & SIGNIFICANCE

THEORETICAL FRAMEWORK

POTENTIAL CO-AUTHORS

KEY WORDS FOR
LITERATURE REVIEW

METHODOLOGY

PROJECTED HYPOTHESES

RESEARCH QUESTIONS

ANALYSIS PLAN

LIMITATIONS

FUTURE DIRECTIONS

PROSPECTIVE PUBLICATIONS

RESEARCH & WRITING SCHEDULE

PROPOSED TITLE

BRAINSTORM

STUDY JUSTIFICATION & SIGNIFICANCE

THEORETICAL FRAMEWORK

PROJECTED HYPOTHESES

POTENTIAL CO-AUTHORS

KEY WORDS FOR LITERATURE REVIEW

RESEARCH QUESTIONS

METHODOLOGY

ANALYSIS PLAN

LIMITATIONS

FUTURE DIRECTIONS

PROSPECTIVE PUBLICATIONS

RESEARCH & WRITING SCHEDULE

PROPOSED TITLE

BRAINSTORM

STUDY JUSTIFICATION & SIGNIFICANCE

THEORETICAL FRAMEWORK

PROJECTED HYPOTHESES

POTENTIAL CO-AUTHORS

KEY WORDS FOR LITERATURE REVIEW

RESEARCH QUESTIONS

METHODOLOGY

ANALYSIS PLAN

LIMITATIONS

FUTURE DIRECTIONS

PROSPECTIVE PUBLICATIONS

RESEARCH & WRITING SCHEDULE

RESEARCH NOTES

PROPOSED TITLE

BRAINSTORM

STUDY JUSTIFICATION & SIGNIFICANCE

THEORETICAL FRAMEWORK

POTENTIAL CO-AUTHORS

KEY WORDS FOR LITERATURE REVIEW

METHODOLOGY

PROJECTED HYPOTHESES

RESEARCH QUESTIONS

ANALYSIS PLAN

LIMITATIONS

FUTURE DIRECTIONS

PROSPECTIVE PUBLICATIONS

RESEARCH & WRITING SCHEDULE

RESEARCH NOTES

PROPOSED TITLE

BRAINSTORM

STUDY JUSTIFICATION & SIGNIFICANCE

THEORETICAL FRAMEWORK

PROJECTED HYPOTHESES

POTENTIAL CO-AUTHORS

KEY WORDS FOR LITERATURE REVIEW

RESEARCH QUESTIONS

METHODOLOGY

ANALYSIS PLAN

LIMITATIONS

FUTURE DIRECTIONS

PROSPECTIVE PUBLICATIONS

RESEARCH & WRITING SCHEDULE

PROPOSED TITLE

BRAINSTORM

STUDY JUSTIFICATION & SIGNIFICANCE

THEORETICAL FRAMEWORK

POTENTIAL CO-AUTHORS

KEY WORDS FOR LITERATURE REVIEW

METHODOLOGY

PROJECTED HYPOTHESES

RESEARCH QUESTIONS

ANALYSIS PLAN

LIMITATIONS

FUTURE DIRECTIONS

PROSPECTIVE PUBLICATIONS

RESEARCH & WRITING SCHEDULE

PROPOSED TITLE

BRAINSTORM

STUDY JUSTIFICATION & SIGNIFICANCE

THEORETICAL FRAMEWORK

PROJECTED HYPOTHESES

POTENTIAL CO-AUTHORS

KEY WORDS FOR LITERATURE REVIEW

RESEARCH QUESTIONS

METHODOLOGY

ANALYSIS PLAN

LIMITATIONS

FUTURE DIRECTIONS

PROSPECTIVE PUBLICATIONS

RESEARCH & WRITING SCHEDULE

RESEARCH NOTES

PROPOSED TITLE

BRAINSTORM

STUDY JUSTIFICATION & SIGNIFICANCE

THEORETICAL FRAMEWORK

PROJECTED HYPOTHESES

POTENTIAL CO-AUTHORS

KEY WORDS FOR LITERATURE REVIEW

RESEARCH QUESTIONS

METHODOLOGY

ANALYSIS PLAN

LIMITATIONS

FUTURE DIRECTIONS

PROSPECTIVE PUBLICATIONS

RESEARCH & WRITING SCHEDULE

PROPOSED TITLE

BRAINSTORM

STUDY JUSTIFICATION & SIGNIFICANCE

THEORETICAL FRAMEWORK

POTENTIAL CO-AUTHORS

KEY WORDS FOR LITERATURE REVIEW

METHODOLOGY

PROJECTED HYPOTHESES

RESEARCH QUESTIONS

ANALYSIS PLAN

LIMITATIONS

FUTURE DIRECTIONS

PROSPECTIVE PUBLICATIONS

RESEARCH & WRITING SCHEDULE

PROPOSED TITLE

BRAINSTORM

STUDY JUSTIFICATION & SIGNIFICANCE

THEORETICAL FRAMEWORK

PROJECTED HYPOTHESES

POTENTIAL CO-AUTHORS

KEY WORDS FOR LITERATURE REVIEW

RESEARCH QUESTIONS

METHODOLOGY

ANALYSIS PLAN

LIMITATIONS

FUTURE DIRECTIONS

PROSPECTIVE PUBLICATIONS

RESEARCH & WRITING SCHEDULE

PROPOSED TITLE

BRAINSTORM

STUDY JUSTIFICATION & SIGNIFICANCE

THEORETICAL FRAMEWORK

PROJECTED HYPOTHESES

POTENTIAL CO-AUTHORS

KEY WORDS FOR LITERATURE REVIEW

RESEARCH QUESTIONS

METHODOLOGY

ANALYSIS PLAN

LIMITATIONS

FUTURE DIRECTIONS

PROSPECTIVE PUBLICATIONS

RESEARCH & WRITING SCHEDULE

RESEARCH NOTES

RESEARCH NOTES

PROPOSED TITLE

BRAINSTORM

STUDY JUSTIFICATION & SIGNIFICANCE

THEORETICAL FRAMEWORK

PROJECTED HYPOTHESES

POTENTIAL CO-AUTHORS

KEY WORDS FOR LITERATURE REVIEW

RESEARCH QUESTIONS

METHODOLOGY

ANALYSIS PLAN

LIMITATIONS

FUTURE DIRECTIONS

PROSPECTIVE PUBLICATIONS

RESEARCH & WRITING SCHEDULE

PROPOSED TITLE

BRAINSTORM

STUDY JUSTIFICATION & SIGNIFICANCE

THEORETICAL FRAMEWORK

PROJECTED HYPOTHESES

POTENTIAL CO-AUTHORS

KEY WORDS FOR LITERATURE REVIEW

RESEARCH QUESTIONS

METHODOLOGY

ANALYSIS PLAN

LIMITATIONS

FUTURE DIRECTIONS

PROSPECTIVE PUBLICATIONS

RESEARCH & WRITING SCHEDULE

PROSPECTIVE PUBLICATIONS

PROPOSED TITLE

BRAINSTORM

STUDY JUSTIFICATION & SIGNIFICANCE

THEORETICAL FRAMEWORK

PROJECTED HYPOTHESES

POTENTIAL CO-AUTHORS

KEY WORDS FOR LITERATURE REVIEW

RESEARCH QUESTIONS

METHODOLOGY

ANALYSIS PLAN

LIMITATIONS

FUTURE DIRECTIONS

PROSPECTIVE PUBLICATIONS

RESEARCH & WRITING SCHEDULE

PROPOSED TITLE

BRAINSTORM

STUDY JUSTIFICATION & SIGNIFICANCE

THEORETICAL FRAMEWORK

PROJECTED HYPOTHESES

POTENTIAL CO-AUTHORS

KEY WORDS FOR LITERATURE REVIEW

RESEARCH QUESTIONS

METHODOLOGY

ANALYSIS PLAN

LIMITATIONS

FUTURE DIRECTIONS

PROSPECTIVE PUBLICATIONS

RESEARCH & WRITING SCHEDULE

PROSPECTIVE PUBLICATIONS

PROPOSED TITLE

BRAINSTORM

STUDY JUSTIFICATION & SIGNIFICANCE

THEORETICAL FRAMEWORK

POTENTIAL CO-AUTHORS

KEY WORDS FOR LITERATURE REVIEW

METHODOLOGY

PROJECTED HYPOTHESES

RESEARCH QUESTIONS

ANALYSIS PLAN

LIMITATIONS

FUTURE DIRECTIONS

PROSPECTIVE PUBLICATIONS

RESEARCH & WRITING SCHEDULE

PROPOSED TITLE

BRAINSTORM

STUDY JUSTIFICATION & SIGNIFICANCE

THEORETICAL FRAMEWORK

PROJECTED HYPOTHESES

POTENTIAL CO-AUTHORS

KEY WORDS FOR LITERATURE REVIEW

RESEARCH QUESTIONS

METHODOLOGY

ANALYSIS PLAN

LIMITATIONS

FUTURE DIRECTIONS

PROSPECTIVE PUBLICATIONS

RESEARCH & WRITING SCHEDULE

PROPOSED TITLE

BRAINSTORM

STUDY JUSTIFICATION & SIGNIFICANCE

THEORETICAL FRAMEWORK

PROJECTED HYPOTHESES

POTENTIAL CO-AUTHORS

KEY WORDS FOR LITERATURE REVIEW

RESEARCH QUESTIONS

METHODOLOGY

ANALYSIS PLAN

LIMITATIONS

FUTURE DIRECTIONS

PROSPECTIVE PUBLICATIONS

RESEARCH & WRITING SCHEDULE

PROSPECTIVE PUBLICATIONS

PROPOSED TITLE

BRAINSTORM

STUDY JUSTIFICATION & SIGNIFICANCE

THEORETICAL FRAMEWORK

PROJECTED HYPOTHESES

POTENTIAL CO-AUTHORS

KEY WORDS FOR LITERATURE REVIEW

RESEARCH QUESTIONS

METHODOLOGY

ANALYSIS PLAN

LIMITATIONS

FUTURE DIRECTIONS

PROSPECTIVE PUBLICATIONS

RESEARCH & WRITING SCHEDULE

PROSPECTIVE PUBLICATIONS

PROPOSED TITLE

BRAINSTORM

STUDY JUSTIFICATION & SIGNIFICANCE

THEORETICAL FRAMEWORK

POTENTIAL CO-AUTHORS

KEY WORDS FOR LITERATURE REVIEW

METHODOLOGY

PROJECTED HYPOTHESES

RESEARCH QUESTIONS

ANALYSIS PLAN

LIMITATIONS

FUTURE DIRECTIONS

PROSPECTIVE PUBLICATIONS

RESEARCH & WRITING SCHEDULE

RESEARCH NOTES

PROPOSED TITLE

BRAINSTORM

STUDY JUSTIFICATION & SIGNIFICANCE

THEORETICAL FRAMEWORK

PROJECTED HYPOTHESES

POTENTIAL CO-AUTHORS

KEY WORDS FOR LITERATURE REVIEW

RESEARCH QUESTIONS

METHODOLOGY

ANALYSIS PLAN

LIMITATIONS

FUTURE DIRECTIONS

PROSPECTIVE PUBLICATIONS

RESEARCH & WRITING SCHEDULE

PROSPECTIVE PUBLICATIONS

PROPOSED TITLE

BRAINSTORM

STUDY JUSTIFICATION & SIGNIFICANCE

THEORETICAL FRAMEWORK

PROJECTED HYPOTHESES

POTENTIAL CO-AUTHORS

KEY WORDS FOR LITERATURE REVIEW

RESEARCH QUESTIONS

METHODOLOGY

ANALYSIS PLAN

LIMITATIONS

FUTURE DIRECTIONS

PROSPECTIVE PUBLICATIONS

RESEARCH & WRITING SCHEDULE

PROSPECTIVE PUBLICATIONS

PROPOSED TITLE

BRAINSTORM

STUDY JUSTIFICATION & SIGNIFICANCE

THEORETICAL FRAMEWORK

PROJECTED HYPOTHESES

POTENTIAL CO-AUTHORS

KEY WORDS FOR LITERATURE REVIEW

RESEARCH QUESTIONS

METHODOLOGY

ANALYSIS PLAN

LIMITATIONS

FUTURE DIRECTIONS

PROSPECTIVE PUBLICATIONS

RESEARCH & WRITING SCHEDULE

RESEARCH NOTES

PROPOSED TITLE

BRAINSTORM

STUDY JUSTIFICATION & SIGNIFICANCE

THEORETICAL FRAMEWORK

PROJECTED HYPOTHESES

POTENTIAL CO-AUTHORS

KEY WORDS FOR LITERATURE REVIEW

RESEARCH QUESTIONS

METHODOLOGY

ANALYSIS PLAN

LIMITATIONS

FUTURE DIRECTIONS

PROSPECTIVE PUBLICATIONS

RESEARCH & WRITING SCHEDULE

PROPOSED TITLE

BRAINSTORM

STUDY JUSTIFICATION & SIGNIFICANCE

THEORETICAL FRAMEWORK

POTENTIAL CO-AUTHORS

KEY WORDS FOR LITERATURE REVIEW

METHODOLOGY

PROJECTED HYPOTHESES

RESEARCH QUESTIONS

ANALYSIS PLAN

LIMITATIONS

FUTURE DIRECTIONS

PROSPECTIVE PUBLICATIONS

RESEARCH & WRITING SCHEDULE

PROPOSED TITLE

BRAINSTORM

STUDY JUSTIFICATION & SIGNIFICANCE

THEORETICAL FRAMEWORK

POTENTIAL CO-AUTHORS

KEY WORDS FOR LITERATURE REVIEW

METHODOLOGY

PROJECTED HYPOTHESES

RESEARCH QUESTIONS

ANALYSIS PLAN

LIMITATIONS

FUTURE DIRECTIONS

PROSPECTIVE PUBLICATIONS

RESEARCH & WRITING SCHEDULE

RESEARCH NOTES

PROPOSED TITLE

BRAINSTORM

STUDY JUSTIFICATION & SIGNIFICANCE

THEORETICAL FRAMEWORK

PROJECTED HYPOTHESES

POTENTIAL CO-AUTHORS

KEY WORDS FOR LITERATURE REVIEW

RESEARCH QUESTIONS

METHODOLOGY

ANALYSIS PLAN

LIMITATIONS

FUTURE DIRECTIONS

PROSPECTIVE PUBLICATIONS

RESEARCH & WRITING SCHEDULE

PROPOSED TITLE

BRAINSTORM

STUDY JUSTIFICATION & SIGNIFICANCE

THEORETICAL FRAMEWORK

PROJECTED HYPOTHESES

POTENTIAL CO-AUTHORS

KEY WORDS FOR LITERATURE REVIEW

RESEARCH QUESTIONS

METHODOLOGY

ANALYSIS PLAN

LIMITATIONS

FUTURE DIRECTIONS

PROSPECTIVE PUBLICATIONS

RESEARCH & WRITING SCHEDULE

PROSPECTIVE PUBLICATIONS

RESEARCH NOTES

PROPOSED TITLE

BRAINSTORM

STUDY JUSTIFICATION & SIGNIFICANCE

THEORETICAL FRAMEWORK

PROJECTED HYPOTHESES

POTENTIAL CO-AUTHORS

**KEY WORDS FOR
LITERATURE REVIEW**

RESEARCH QUESTIONS

METHODOLOGY

ANALYSIS PLAN

LIMITATIONS

FUTURE DIRECTIONS

PROSPECTIVE PUBLICATIONS

RESEARCH & WRITING SCHEDULE

RESEARCH NOTES

PROPOSED TITLE

BRAINSTORM

STUDY JUSTIFICATION & SIGNIFICANCE

THEORETICAL FRAMEWORK

PROJECTED HYPOTHESES

POTENTIAL CO-AUTHORS

KEY WORDS FOR LITERATURE REVIEW

RESEARCH QUESTIONS

METHODOLOGY

ANALYSIS PLAN

LIMITATIONS

FUTURE DIRECTIONS

PROSPECTIVE PUBLICATIONS

RESEARCH & WRITING SCHEDULE

RESEARCH NOTES

PROPOSED TITLE

BRAINSTORM

STUDY JUSTIFICATION & SIGNIFICANCE

THEORETICAL FRAMEWORK

POTENTIAL CO-AUTHORS

KEY WORDS FOR LITERATURE REVIEW

METHODOLOGY

PROJECTED HYPOTHESES

RESEARCH QUESTIONS

ANALYSIS PLAN

LIMITATIONS

FUTURE DIRECTIONS

PROSPECTIVE PUBLICATIONS

RESEARCH & WRITING SCHEDULE

PROPOSED TITLE

BRAINSTORM

STUDY JUSTIFICATION & SIGNIFICANCE

THEORETICAL FRAMEWORK

PROJECTED HYPOTHESES

POTENTIAL CO-AUTHORS

KEY WORDS FOR LITERATURE REVIEW

RESEARCH QUESTIONS

METHODOLOGY

ANALYSIS PLAN

LIMITATIONS

FUTURE DIRECTIONS

PROSPECTIVE PUBLICATIONS

RESEARCH & WRITING SCHEDULE

RESEARCH NOTES

PROPOSED TITLE

BRAINSTORM

STUDY JUSTIFICATION & SIGNIFICANCE

THEORETICAL FRAMEWORK

PROJECTED HYPOTHESES

POTENTIAL CO-AUTHORS

**KEY WORDS FOR
LITERATURE REVIEW**

RESEARCH QUESTIONS

METHODOLOGY

ANALYSIS PLAN

LIMITATIONS

FUTURE DIRECTIONS

PROSPECTIVE PUBLICATIONS

RESEARCH & WRITING SCHEDULE

RESEARCH NOTES

PROPOSED TITLE

BRAINSTORM

STUDY JUSTIFICATION & SIGNIFICANCE

THEORETICAL FRAMEWORK

PROJECTED HYPOTHESES

POTENTIAL CO-AUTHORS

KEY WORDS FOR LITERATURE REVIEW

RESEARCH QUESTIONS

METHODOLOGY

ANALYSIS PLAN

LIMITATIONS

FUTURE DIRECTIONS

PROSPECTIVE PUBLICATIONS

RESEARCH & WRITING SCHEDULE

RESEARCH NOTES

RESEARCH NOTES

PROPOSED TITLE

BRAINSTORM

STUDY JUSTIFICATION & SIGNIFICANCE

THEORETICAL FRAMEWORK

PROJECTED HYPOTHESES

POTENTIAL CO-AUTHORS

**KEY WORDS FOR
LITERATURE REVIEW**

RESEARCH QUESTIONS

METHODOLOGY

ANALYSIS PLAN

LIMITATIONS

FUTURE DIRECTIONS

PROSPECTIVE PUBLICATIONS

RESEARCH & WRITING SCHEDULE

PROPOSED TITLE

BRAINSTORM

STUDY JUSTIFICATION & SIGNIFICANCE

THEORETICAL FRAMEWORK

POTENTIAL CO-AUTHORS

KEY WORDS FOR
LITERATURE REVIEW

METHODOLOGY

PROJECTED HYPOTHESES

RESEARCH QUESTIONS

ANALYSIS PLAN

LIMITATIONS

FUTURE DIRECTIONS

PROSPECTIVE PUBLICATIONS

RESEARCH & WRITING SCHEDULE

PROPOSED TITLE

BRAINSTORM

STUDY JUSTIFICATION & SIGNIFICANCE

THEORETICAL FRAMEWORK

PROJECTED HYPOTHESES

POTENTIAL CO-AUTHORS

KEY WORDS FOR LITERATURE REVIEW

RESEARCH QUESTIONS

METHODOLOGY

ANALYSIS PLAN

LIMITATIONS

FUTURE DIRECTIONS

PROSPECTIVE PUBLICATIONS

RESEARCH & WRITING SCHEDULE

PROPOSED TITLE

BRAINSTORM

STUDY JUSTIFICATION & SIGNIFICANCE

THEORETICAL FRAMEWORK

POTENTIAL CO-AUTHORS

KEY WORDS FOR LITERATURE REVIEW

METHODOLOGY

PROJECTED HYPOTHESES

RESEARCH QUESTIONS

ANALYSIS PLAN

LIMITATIONS

FUTURE DIRECTIONS

PROSPECTIVE PUBLICATIONS

RESEARCH & WRITING SCHEDULE

RESEARCH NOTES

PROPOSED TITLE

BRAINSTORM

STUDY JUSTIFICATION & SIGNIFICANCE

THEORETICAL FRAMEWORK

PROJECTED HYPOTHESES

POTENTIAL CO-AUTHORS

KEY WORDS FOR LITERATURE REVIEW

RESEARCH QUESTIONS

METHODOLOGY

ANALYSIS PLAN

LIMITATIONS

FUTURE DIRECTIONS

PROSPECTIVE PUBLICATIONS

RESEARCH & WRITING SCHEDULE

PROPOSED TITLE

BRAINSTORM

STUDY JUSTIFICATION & SIGNIFICANCE

THEORETICAL FRAMEWORK

POTENTIAL CO-AUTHORS

KEY WORDS FOR LITERATURE REVIEW

METHODOLOGY

PROJECTED HYPOTHESES

RESEARCH QUESTIONS

ANALYSIS PLAN

LIMITATIONS

FUTURE DIRECTIONS

PROSPECTIVE PUBLICATIONS

RESEARCH & WRITING SCHEDULE

RESEARCH NOTES

RESEARCH NOTES

PROPOSED TITLE

BRAINSTORM

STUDY JUSTIFICATION & SIGNIFICANCE

THEORETICAL FRAMEWORK

PROJECTED HYPOTHESES

POTENTIAL CO-AUTHORS

KEY WORDS FOR
LITERATURE REVIEW

RESEARCH QUESTIONS

METHODOLOGY

ANALYSIS PLAN

LIMITATIONS

FUTURE DIRECTIONS

PROSPECTIVE PUBLICATIONS

RESEARCH & WRITING SCHEDULE

PROSPECTIVE PUBLICATIONS

PROPOSED TITLE

BRAINSTORM

STUDY JUSTIFICATION & SIGNIFICANCE

THEORETICAL FRAMEWORK

POTENTIAL CO-AUTHORS

KEY WORDS FOR LITERATURE REVIEW

METHODOLOGY

PROJECTED HYPOTHESES

RESEARCH QUESTIONS

ANALYSIS PLAN

LIMITATIONS

FUTURE DIRECTIONS

PROSPECTIVE PUBLICATIONS

RESEARCH & WRITING SCHEDULE

PROPOSED TITLE

BRAINSTORM

STUDY JUSTIFICATION & SIGNIFICANCE

THEORETICAL FRAMEWORK

PROJECTED HYPOTHESES

POTENTIAL CO-AUTHORS

KEY WORDS FOR LITERATURE REVIEW

RESEARCH QUESTIONS

METHODOLOGY

ANALYSIS PLAN

LIMITATIONS

FUTURE DIRECTIONS

PROSPECTIVE PUBLICATIONS

RESEARCH & WRITING SCHEDULE

RESEARCH NOTES

PROPOSED TITLE

BRAINSTORM

STUDY JUSTIFICATION & SIGNIFICANCE

THEORETICAL FRAMEWORK

PROJECTED HYPOTHESES

POTENTIAL CO-AUTHORS

KEY WORDS FOR LITERATURE REVIEW

RESEARCH QUESTIONS

METHODOLOGY

ANALYSIS PLAN

LIMITATIONS

FUTURE DIRECTIONS

PROSPECTIVE PUBLICATIONS

RESEARCH & WRITING SCHEDULE

PROPOSED TITLE

BRAINSTORM

STUDY JUSTIFICATION & SIGNIFICANCE

THEORETICAL FRAMEWORK

POTENTIAL CO-AUTHORS

KEY WORDS FOR LITERATURE REVIEW

METHODOLOGY

PROJECTED HYPOTHESES

RESEARCH QUESTIONS

ANALYSIS PLAN

LIMITATIONS

FUTURE DIRECTIONS

PROSPECTIVE PUBLICATIONS

RESEARCH & WRITING SCHEDULE

PROPOSED TITLE

BRAINSTORM

STUDY JUSTIFICATION & SIGNIFICANCE

THEORETICAL FRAMEWORK

PROJECTED HYPOTHESES

POTENTIAL CO-AUTHORS

KEY WORDS FOR
LITERATURE REVIEW

RESEARCH QUESTIONS

METHODOLOGY

ANALYSIS PLAN

LIMITATIONS

FUTURE DIRECTIONS

PROSPECTIVE PUBLICATIONS

RESEARCH & WRITING SCHEDULE

PROPOSED TITLE

BRAINSTORM

STUDY JUSTIFICATION & SIGNIFICANCE

THEORETICAL FRAMEWORK

POTENTIAL CO-AUTHORS

KEY WORDS FOR LITERATURE REVIEW

METHODOLOGY

PROJECTED HYPOTHESES

RESEARCH QUESTIONS

ANALYSIS PLAN

LIMITATIONS

FUTURE DIRECTIONS

PROSPECTIVE PUBLICATIONS

RESEARCH & WRITING SCHEDULE

PROPOSED TITLE

BRAINSTORM

STUDY JUSTIFICATION & SIGNIFICANCE

THEORETICAL FRAMEWORK

PROJECTED HYPOTHESES

POTENTIAL CO-AUTHORS

KEY WORDS FOR LITERATURE REVIEW

RESEARCH QUESTIONS

METHODOLOGY

ANALYSIS PLAN

LIMITATIONS

FUTURE DIRECTIONS

PROSPECTIVE PUBLICATIONS

RESEARCH & WRITING SCHEDULE

PROPOSED TITLE

BRAINSTORM

STUDY JUSTIFICATION & SIGNIFICANCE

THEORETICAL FRAMEWORK

PROJECTED HYPOTHESES

POTENTIAL CO-AUTHORS

KEY WORDS FOR LITERATURE REVIEW

RESEARCH QUESTIONS

METHODOLOGY

ANALYSIS PLAN

LIMITATIONS

FUTURE DIRECTIONS

PROSPECTIVE PUBLICATIONS

RESEARCH & WRITING SCHEDULE

PROPOSED TITLE

BRAINSTORM

STUDY JUSTIFICATION & SIGNIFICANCE

THEORETICAL FRAMEWORK

PROJECTED HYPOTHESES

POTENTIAL CO-AUTHORS

KEY WORDS FOR LITERATURE REVIEW

RESEARCH QUESTIONS

METHODOLOGY

ANALYSIS PLAN

LIMITATIONS

FUTURE DIRECTIONS

PROSPECTIVE PUBLICATIONS

RESEARCH & WRITING SCHEDULE

PROPOSED TITLE

BRAINSTORM

STUDY JUSTIFICATION & SIGNIFICANCE

THEORETICAL FRAMEWORK

PROJECTED HYPOTHESES

POTENTIAL CO-AUTHORS

KEY WORDS FOR LITERATURE REVIEW

RESEARCH QUESTIONS

METHODOLOGY

ANALYSIS PLAN

LIMITATIONS

FUTURE DIRECTIONS

PROSPECTIVE PUBLICATIONS

RESEARCH & WRITING SCHEDULE

PROSPECTIVE PUBLICATIONS

PROPOSED TITLE

BRAINSTORM

STUDY JUSTIFICATION & SIGNIFICANCE

THEORETICAL FRAMEWORK

PROJECTED HYPOTHESES

POTENTIAL CO-AUTHORS

**KEY WORDS FOR
LITERATURE REVIEW**

RESEARCH QUESTIONS

METHODOLOGY

ANALYSIS PLAN

LIMITATIONS

FUTURE DIRECTIONS

PROSPECTIVE PUBLICATIONS

RESEARCH & WRITING SCHEDULE

PROPOSED TITLE

BRAINSTORM

STUDY JUSTIFICATION & SIGNIFICANCE

THEORETICAL FRAMEWORK

PROJECTED HYPOTHESES

POTENTIAL CO-AUTHORS

KEY WORDS FOR LITERATURE REVIEW

RESEARCH QUESTIONS

METHODOLOGY

ANALYSIS PLAN

LIMITATIONS

FUTURE DIRECTIONS

PROSPECTIVE PUBLICATIONS

RESEARCH & WRITING SCHEDULE

RESEARCH NOTES

Made in the USA
Middletown, DE
20 September 2020